Throughout her life, artist Vy Zwier
has found ways to breathe
her passion for art and creativity
into her life and the lives of
those around her.

From drawing, tattooing, photography,
to digital media,
Vy's artistic mark is indelible.
Her portfolio spans a wide range of mediums,
but her true love
is putting pen to paper, or iPad and
allowing her creativity to flow freely across the pages.

Lost Love Designs is a heartfelt endeavor
to heal, bringing love and light
to the forefront of our everyday experiences.
Each unique, hand drawn mandala is created to
honor the small moments of romance
that take your breath away.

It is with sincere gratitude
that this book is offered to you.
With the hope that you too, will find
healing and love within these pages.